Success
10 Minute Tests

English

age 7–8 · levels 1–3

Alison Head

Sample page

clear instructional text

topic being covered

test number for quick reference

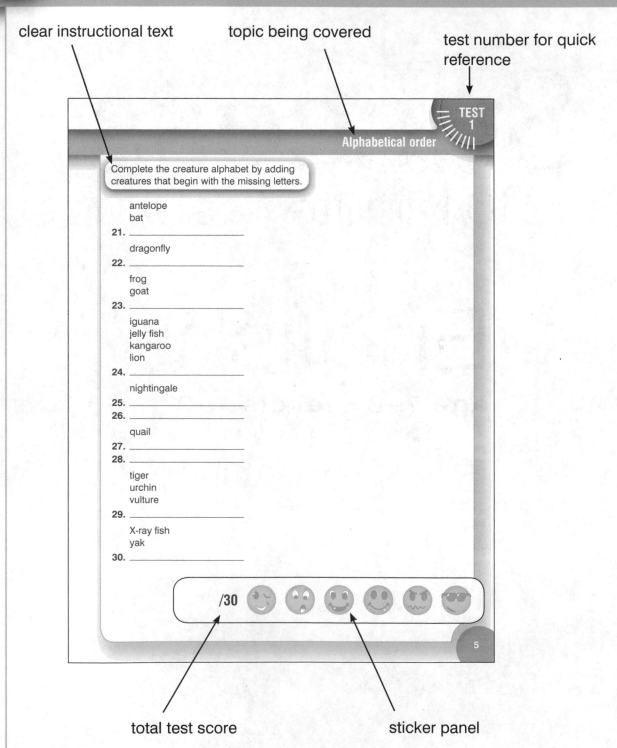

TEST 1

Alphabetical order

Complete the creature alphabet by adding creatures that begin with the missing letters.

antelope
bat
21. _____

dragonfly
22. _____

frog
goat
23. _____

iguana
jelly fish
kangaroo
lion
24. _____

nightingale
25. _____
26. _____

quail
27. _____
28. _____

tiger
urchin
vulture
29. _____

X-ray fish
yak
30. _____

/30

5

total test score

sticker panel

Contents

Ten letters are missing from this alphabet.
Write the missing letters in the boxes below.

a b _____ _____ e _____ g h _____ j _____ l _____ n o _____ q r s _____ u _____ w x _____ z

1.	2.	3.	4.	5.
6.	7.	8.	9.	10.

Write the words in the box below, in the correct alphabetical order.

piano	football	flower	chair	box
holiday	horse	carpet	pencil	bunch

11. _____

12. _____

13. _____

14. _____

15. _____

16. _____

17. _____

18. _____

19. _____

20. _____

Complete the creature alphabet by adding creatures that begin with the missing letters.

antelope
bat
21. _____

dragonfly
22. _____

frog
goat
23. _____

iguana
jelly fish
kangaroo
lion
24. _____

nightingale
25. _____
26. _____

quail
27. _____
28. _____

tiger
urchin
vulture
29. _____

X-ray fish
yak
30. _____

/30

Verbs are doing words, like **run** or **sing**. Underline the verb in each sentence.

1. Rain makes puddles in the street.
2. Our cat sleeps on my bed.
3. My brother's teacher is funny.
4. I want a football for my birthday.
5. Dad reads the newspaper each morning.
6. Tim loves skateboarding.
7. The goalkeeper guards the goal.
8. Our class bakes cakes at school.
9. Amy buys a comic each Friday.
10. Eve finds pretty shells at the beach.

Pick a verb from the box with a similar meaning to each of the verbs listed below.

	fall	find	collect
run	answer	shout	arrange
	mend	hurry	give

11. reply _____

12. tumble _____

13. gather _____

14. repair _____

15. donate _____

16. sprint _____

17. yell _____

18. organise _____

19. rush _____

20. locate _____

Tick the box by the verb which best completes each sentence.

21. Grandad always _____ me a card on my birthday.

☐ sells ☐ sends ☐ lends

22. My toy boat _____ on the lake.

☐ flies ☐ sinks ☐ floats

23. We _____ our cat to the vet when he is ill.

☐ take ☐ mend ☐ find

24. I always _____ my room on Saturdays.

☐ drop ☐ wash ☐ tidy

25. It is important to _____ your teeth twice a day.

☐ waste ☐ brush ☐ sweep

26. The bus _____ at the end of our street.

☐ stops ☐ ends ☐ follows

27. Our dog loves to _____ her tail.

☐ follow ☐ copy ☐ chase

28. It _____ lovely when it snows.

☐ is ☐ will ☐ are

29. Alex _____ it will be sunny tomorrow.

☐ likes ☐ hopes ☐ wants

30. Birds _____ in nests in the trees.

☐ live ☐ fly ☐ build

/30

Verb tenses

We use the past tense to write about things that have already happened. Complete these word sums to turn present tense verbs into past tense verbs. You may need to change the spelling of some verbs first.

1. wait + ed = _____

2. walk + ed = _____

3. climb + ed = _____

4. look + ed = _____

5. pack + ed = _____

6. shout + ed = _____

7. wish + ed = _____

8. smile + ed = _____

9. rule + ed = _____

10. bake + ed = _____

Draw lines to match each verb with the correct past tense verb.

11. fail	came
12. see	climbed
13. make	looked
14. come	packed
15. walk	saw
16. climb	found
17. look	walked
18. pack	wrote
19. write	failed
20. find	made

Circle the correct past tense version of each of the verbs in bold.

21. tell	telled	told
22. fall	fell	fall
23. lose	lost	losed
24. bring	bringed	brought
25. catch	caught	catched

Write these sentences again, with a past tense verb instead of the bold present tense verb.

26. The boys **want** to play outside.

_____

27. Actors **perform** in the theatre every weekend.

_____

28. Families **buy** all of the bread in the bakery.

_____

29. I **draw** pictures in my spare time.

_____

30. We **know** our times tables.

_____

/30

Adding *ing*

> Underline the verb that ends with **ing** in each sentence.

1. It was snowing on my birthday.
2. Auntie Kath is bringing balloons for the party.
3. I love my dancing lessons.
4. Dad is taking the car to the garage.
5. Greg was writing a letter to his friend.
6. Laughing, the girls jumped into the pool.
7. We are buying new shoes after school.
8. Mum is growing vegetables in the garden.
9. Samia is saving her pocket money for a new bike.
10. We were waiting for the bus for half an hour.

> Circle the extra letter that has been added when **ing** is joined to each verb.

11. win   winn*ing*
12. dig   digg*ing*
13. tap   tapp*ing*
14. beg   begg*ing*
15. shut   shutt*ing*
16. swim   swimm*ing*
17. run   runn*ing*
18. hop   hopp*ing*
19. grab   grabb*ing*
20. shop   shopp*ing*

ing has been added to these words too.
Write the letter that has been removed in the box.

21. make   ma*k*ing   ☐

22. bite   bi*t*ing   ☐

23. poke   po*k*ing   ☐

24. like   li*k*ing   ☐

25. hope   ho*p*ing   ☐

26. shake   sha*k*ing   ☐

27. rake   ra*k*ing   ☐

28. smile   smi*l*ing   ☐

29. skate   ska*t*ing   ☐

30. cope   co*p*ing   ☐

Complete these word sums.

31. create + ing = _____

32. find + ing = _____

33. come + ing = _____

34. sit + ing = _____

35. hum + ing = _____

36. fit + ing = _____

37. bake + ing = _____

38. stop + ing = _____

39. grin + ing = _____

40. flap + ing = _____

/40

Word endings **el**, **al** and **le** can often sound the same. Sort these words into **el**, **al** and **le** endings.

1. hospital	**2.** label
3. stable	**4.** table
5. festival	**6.** medical
7. model	**8.** level
9. loyal	**10.** purple
11. travel	**12.** ankle

el ending	**al** ending	**le** ending

Circle the correctly spelled word in each pair.

13. abel	able	
14. local	locel	
15. novle	novel	
16. carnival	carnivle	
17. coupel	couple	
18. medle	medal	
19. petal	petel	
20. royle	royal	

Complete each word with **al** or **le**.

21. alphabetic_____

22. app_____

23. nibb_____

24. foc_____

25. tot_____

26. crad_____

27. re_____

28. litt_____

29. gener_____

30. tit_____

Write these words again, with the correctly spelled ending.

31. rattel   _____

32. legle   _____

33. bubbel   _____

34. metel   _____

35. crackal   _____

36. hotle   _____

37. criticel   _____

38. fatel   _____

39. magicle   _____

40. focel   _____

/40

Prefixes

A prefix is a group of letters that you can add to the start of a word to change its meaning. Underline the prefix in each word.

1. unhappy

2. preview

3. renew

4. unsure

5. export

6. disappoint

7. mistake

8. exchange

9. unkind

10. reapply

Choose a prefix **un** or **dis** to add to each word.

11. _____realistic

12. _____fair

13. _____approve

14. _____prove

15. _____natural

16. _____obey

17. _____worn

18. _____honest

19. _____lock

20. _____honour

Find and copy ten words in this piece of text that begin with a prefix.

The accident happened at school when we went to exchange our library books. Billy began to misbehave and would not cooperate with the teacher. Mr West explained that his behaviour was unnecessary and unhelpful but it made no difference.

Billy pushed Daniel and unfortunately, he fell over, grazing his knee. The school nurse was unavailable so Mr West helped Daniel wash his knee with antiseptic. Billy was unhappy that he had hurt Daniel so he said sorry, but Daniel was unwilling to listen.

21. _____   22. _____

23. _____   24. _____

25. _____   26. _____

27. _____   28. _____

29. _____   30. _____

Find the opposite of each word in bold. Circle the correct opposite.

31. **prove**   disprove   unprove

32. **believable**   disbelievable   unbelievable

33. **tasteful**   untasteful   distasteful

34. **pleased**   displeased   antipleased

35. **paid**   nonpaid   unpaid

36. **order**   unorder   disorder

37. **welcome**   unwelcome   antiwelcome

38. **suitable**   dissuitable   unsuitable

39. **own**   disown   unown

40. **plug**   antiplug   unplug

/40

Synonyms

Draw lines to match the pairs of words with similar meanings.

1. small   spooky

2. angry   fast

3. scary   enormous

4. cold   sleepy

5. quick   little

6. pretty   soggy

7. huge   create

8. make   furious

9. tired   beautiful

10. wet   chilly

Write a synonym for each word.

11. happy   _____

12. sad   _____

13. difficult   _____

14. tasty   _____

15. surprised   _____

16. soft   _____

17. risky   _____

18. heroic   _____

19. neat   _____

20. ancient   _____

Write these sentences again, replacing the bold word with a synonym.

21. The blackberry bush was covered with **spiky** thorns.

_____

22. The professor was very **intelligent**.

_____

23. We **rushed** to the bus stop.

_____

24. We **discovered** a lovely beach to play on.

_____

25. The boy **gobbled** the ice-cream.

_____

26. The traffic outside the school was very **loud**.

_____

27. The lake in the park is **circular**.

_____

28. Books were **stacked** up all over the floor.

_____

29. Mum was angry because my bedroom was **messy**.

_____

30. Evie **laughed** at the funny joke.

_____

/30

Underline the words in each sentence that someone has spoken.

1. "Don't forget your lunchbox!" called Mum.

2. Sophie asked, "What time does the film start?"

3. Max snapped, "Leave me alone!"

4. "Good morning, class," said Miss Smith.

5. "Is there any more pizza?" asked Sam.

Draw lines to match the halves of each sentence.

6. "Please may I have a drink?"   asked Dad, looking under a cushion.

7. Molly grumbled,   "That tickles!"

8. Tom giggled,   reminded Mr Greene.

9. "Don't forget to check your answers," asked Joe.

10. "Have you seen my wallet?"   "I'm bored!"

11. "Look at that firework!"   shouted Max, clutching his knee.

12. Looking at the mess, Mum insisted,   shivered Afraz.

13. "Ouch!"   gasped Molly, amazed.

14. "The water is freezing!"   apologised Martin.

15. "I'm sorry I broke your pen,"   "You must tidy your room!"

Add speech marks to these sentences.

16. Let's go bowling, suggested Mum.

17. Where are my football boots? asked Lauren.

18. I hope it won't rain later, worried Daisy.

19. That's mine! shouted Will.

20. I don't want to go to bed! complained Jodie.

Add your own speech with speech marks to these sentences.

21. The shy little girl whispered, _____.

22. The children at the birthday party all shouted, _____.

23. The angry teacher said, _____.

24. When he saw the puppy, the little boy said, _____.

25. Looking at the menu Mum said, _____.

26. Seeing the chocolate cake, Katie said, _____.

27. _____, said Mark to the new boy in the class.

28. _____, complained the bus driver.

29. When she read my school report, Mum said, _____.

30. _____, screamed the children on the rollercoaster.

/30

Sentences

Write each sentence again, adding capital letters and a full stop, question mark, or exclamation mark at the end.

1. it is my birthday tomorrow

_____

2. have you seen my hockey stick

_____

3. your picture is amazing

_____

4. my friend daniel is coming to play after school

_____

5. in march we are going to paris on holiday

_____

6. how do you tie a bow

_____

7. that sandwich is enormous

_____

8. when dad gets home we will all have dinner

_____

9. is it getting dark yet

_____

10. last friday megan had a fantastic party

_____

Write your own sentences about these things using capital letters and punctuation.

11. your best friend

_____

12. your favourite place

_____

13. what you had for breakfast

_____

14. your bedroom

_____

15. rainy days

_____

16. your teacher

_____

17. your favourite food

_____

18. the job you would like when you are older

_____

19. a question you would like to know the answer to

_____

20. something funny that has happened to you

_____

/20

Collective nouns

Collective nouns describe groups of things.
Underline the collective noun in each sentence.

1. A flock of sheep grazed in the field.

2. We took a pack of cards with us for the journey.

3. Our dog has a litter of puppies.

4. Dad bought Mum a bunch of flowers.

5. We saw a pride of lions at the zoo.

6. A swarm of flies crowded round the dustbins.

7. A pod of whales swam past the cruise ship.

8. We have to climb two flights of stairs to reach our classroom.

9. The farm has a herd of dairy cows.

10. A flock of seagulls flew over our heads.

Tick the correct word to complete each well-known collective noun.

11. a _____ of mountains ☐ range ☐ flock

12. a _____ of grapes ☐ bundle ☐ bunch

13. a _____ of stars ☐ range ☐ galaxy

14. an _____ of soldiers ☐ army ☐ class

15. a _____ of geese ☐ bunch ☐ gaggle

16. a _____ of bees ☐ hive ☐ pack

17. a _____ of wolves ☐ pack ☐ litter

18. a _____ of singers ☐ army ☐ choir

19. a _____ of football players ☐ pack ☐ team

20. a _____ of ships ☐ float ☐ fleet

Write a sentence using each of these collective nouns.

21. bunch of bananas

_____

22. class of students

_____

23. shoal of fish

_____

24. forest of trees

_____

25. a library of books

_____

Make up your own clever collective nouns for these things.

26. horses

_____

27. hippos

_____

28. tractors

_____

29. pigs

_____

30. cushions

_____

/30

Consonants are all the letters of the alphabet except the vowels **a**, **e**, **i**, **o** and **u**. Underline the double consonants in each word.

1. bubble
2. hobble
3. riddle
4. muddle
5. litter
6. clatter
7. grinning
8. shudder
9. paddle
10. shutter
11. ripple
12. rabbit
13. hopping
14. letter
15. sudden
16. matter
17. wobble
18. dinner
19. cattle
20. winning

Circle the real word in each pair.

21. comon   common
22. pudle   puddle
23. water   watter
24. stuble   stubble
25. crater   cratter
26. tabble   table
27. nible   nibble
28. adult   addult
29. cutting   cuting
30. shuttle   shutle

Double consonants

Add the missing double consonant to each word.

31. 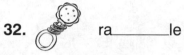 ke_____le

32.  ra_____le

33.  a_____le

34. 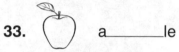 lo_____y

35. 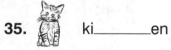 ki_____en

36. 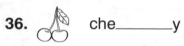 che_____y

37.  na_____y

38.  swi_____er

39. co_____on

40. mi_____en

/40

Fun with collective nouns

Find these words in the word-search grid.

1. bunch
2. herd
3. pack
4. pride
5. flock
6. swarm
7. fleet
8. gaggle
9. litter
10. galaxy

p	e	h	m	k	o	s	e	r	b
r	g	j	v	k	a	e	k	w	u
i	q	k	c	d	m	n	r	r	n
d	u	a	g	a	g	g	l	e	c
e	p	e	a	m	s	s	i	g	h
a	h	f	l	o	c	k	t	c	c
j	t	l	a	w	h	a	t	u	r
h	a	e	x	n	q	e	e	d	o
w	f	e	y	w	l	e	r	h	c
o	l	t	s	w	a	r	m	d	k

Fun with double consonants

Find ten double consonant words hidden in the word snake.

1. _____

2. _____

3. _____

4. _____

5. _____

6. _____

7. _____

8. _____

9. _____

10. _____

Many words end in the suffixes **er** or **est**. Complete these word sums.

1. tall + er   = _____

2. small + est = _____

3. short + est = _____

4. loud + est = _____

5. fast + er   = _____

6. old + est   = _____

7. bright + er = _____

8. young + er = _____

9. great + est = _____

10. cold + er   = _____

Circle the correctly spelled word in each pair.

11. prettier   prettyer

12. bigest   biggest

13. finer   fineer

14. bravest   braveest

15. sillyest   silliest

16. fatest   fattest

17. safer   safeer

18. lovelier   lovelyer

19. spiciest   spicyest

20. hoter   hotter

Complete the chart.

	+ er	+ est
pale	21.	22.
shiny	23.	24.
fussy	25.	26.
wide	27.	28.
flat	29.	30.

Find 10 spelling mistakes in this piece of text, then write the correct words below.

When school started in September, the mornings were already getting chillyer. The lateest I could leave for school was 8.30 a.m. and even then I had to run. I may have been the fitest in my class but I certainly wasn't the earlyest!

The naughtyest boy in my class was called Lee. He had the cheekyest grin and dirtyest hands you have even seen and the teachers were always angryer with him than with anyone else. Lee was the noisyest in the class too, and biger than most of us, so we were all a bit afraid of him.

31. _____

32. _____

33. _____

34. _____

35. _____

36. _____

37. _____

38. _____

39. _____

40. _____

/40

Underline the silent letter in each word.

1. thumb
2. knot
3. gnome
4. sign
5. rhyme
6. write
7. knee
8. calm
9. sword
10. chemist
11. would
12. stalk
13. when
14. scene
15. chalk
16. knock
17. wreck
18. gnaw
19. palm
20. numb

Tick the box next to the correct silent letter to complete each word.

21. fo____k   ☐ l   ☐ m   ☐ g

22. ____nuckle   ☐ r   ☐ k   ☐ w

23. plum____er   ☐ b   ☐ m   ☐ n

24. cou____d   ☐ r   ☐ f   ☐ l

25. ____rist   ☐ w   ☐ t   ☐ l

26. w____ich   ☐ s   ☐ h   ☐ i

27. ____rinkle   ☐ l   ☐ t   ☐ w

28. ____nat   ☐ g   ☐ h   ☐ b

29. wa____k   ☐ w   ☐ l   ☐ g

30. g____ard   ☐ w   ☐ u   ☐ l

Answer booklet: English 10 Minute Tests, age 7–8

Test 1
1–10. missing letters are: c, d, f, i, k, m, p, t, v, y

11. box	**12.** bunch
13. carpet	**14.** chair
15. flower	**16.** football
17. holiday	**18.** horse
19. pencil	**20.** piano

21–30. Answers will vary but might include:

21. cat	**22.** elephant
23. horse	**24.** mouse
25. octopus	**26.** penguin
27. rabbit	**28.** snake
29. whale	**30.** zebra

Test 2
1. Rain <u>makes</u> puddles in the street.
2. Our cat <u>sleeps</u> on my bed.
3. My brother's teacher <u>is</u> funny.
4. I <u>want</u> a football for my birthday.
5. Dad <u>reads</u> the newspaper each morning.
6. Tim <u>loves</u> skateboarding.
7. The goalkeeper <u>guards</u> the goal.
8. Our class <u>bakes</u> cakes at school.
9. Amy <u>buys</u> a comic each Friday.
10. Eve <u>finds</u> pretty shells at the beach.

11. answer	**12.** fall
13. collect	**14.** mend
15. give	**16.** run
17. shout	**18.** arrange
19. hurry	**20.** find
21. sends	**22.** floats
23. take	**24.** tidy
25. brush	**26.** stops
27. chase	**28.** is
29. hopes	**30.** live

Test 3
1. waited	**2.** walked
3. climbed	**4.** looked
5. packed	**6.** shouted
7. wished	**8.** smiled
9. ruled	**10.** baked
11. failed	**12.** saw
13. made	**14.** came
15. walked	**16.** climbed
17. looked	**18.** packed
19. wrote	**20.** found
21. told	**22.** fell
23. lost	**24.** brought
25. caught	

26. The boys wanted to play outside.
27. Actors performed in the theatre every weekend.
28. Families bought all of the bread in the bakery.
29. I drew pictures in my spare time.
30. We knew our times tables.

Test 4
1. snowing	**2.** bringing
3. dancing	**4.** taking
5. writing	**6.** laughing
7. buying	**8.** growing
9. saving	**10.** waiting
11. n	**12.** g
13. p	**14.** g
15. t	**16.** m
17. n	**18.** p
19. b	**20.** p
21–30. e	**31.** creating
32. finding	**33.** coming
34. sitting	**35.** humming
36. fitting	**37.** baking
38. stopping	**39.** grinning
40. flapping	

Test 5
1–12. **el** words: label, model, level, travel
al words: hospital, festival, medical, loyal
le words: stable, table, purple, ankle

13. able	**14.** local
15. novel	**16.** carnival
17. couple	**18.** medal
19. petal	**20.** royal
21. alphabetical	**22.** apple
23. nibble	**24.** focal
25. total	**26.** cradle
27. real	**28.** little
29. general	**30.** title
31. rattle	**32.** legal
33. bubble	**34.** metal
35. crackle	**36.** hotel
37. critical	**38.** fatal
39. magical	**40.** focal

Test 6
1. unhappy	**2.** preview
3. renew	**4.** unsure
5. export	**6.** disappoint
7. mistake	**8.** exchange
9. unkind	**10.** reapply
11. unrealistic	**12.** unfair
13. disapprove	**14.** disprove
15. unnatural	**16.** disobey
17. unworn	**18.** dishonest
19. unlock	**20.** dishonour
21. exchange	**22.** misbehave
23. cooperate	**24.** unnecessary
25. unhelpful	**26.** unfortunately
27. unavailable	**28.** antiseptic
29. unhappy	**30.** unwilling
31. disprove	**32.** unbelievable
33. distasteful	**34.** displeased
35. unpaid	**36.** disorder
37. unwelcome	**38.** unsuitable
39. disown	**40.** unplug

Test 7
1. little	**2.** furious
3. spooky	**4.** chilly
5. fast	**6.** beautiful
7. enormous	**8.** create
9. sleepy	**10.** soggy

11–30. Answers may include:

11. delighted	**12.** unhappy
13. tricky	**14.** delicious
15. shocked	**16.** sllky
17. dangerous	**18.** brave
19. tidy	**20.** old
21. prickly	**22.** clever
23. hurried	**24.** found
25. ate	**26.** noisy
27. round	**28.** piled
29. untidy	**30.** giggled

Test 8
1. "Don't forget your lunchbox!" called Mum.
2. Sophie asked, "What time does the film start?"
3. Max snapped, "Leave me alone!"
4. "Good morning, class," said Miss Smith.
5. "Is there any more pizza?" asked Sam.
6. "Please may I have a drink?" asked Joe.
7. Molly grumbled, "I'm bored!"
8. Tom giggled, "That tickles!"
9. "Don't forget to check your answers," reminded Mr Greene.
10. "Have you seen my wallet?" asked Dad, looking under a cushion.
11. "Look at that firework!" gasped Molly, amazed.
12. Looking at the mess, Mum insisted, "You must tidy your room!"
13. "Ouch!" shouted Max, clutching his knee.
14. "The water is freezing!" shivered Afraz.
15. "I'm sorry I broke your pen," apologised Martin.
16. "Let's go bowling," suggested Mum.
17. "Where are my football boots?" asked Lauren.
18. "I hope it won't rain later," worried Daisy.
19. "That's mine!" shouted Will.
20. "I don't want to go to bed!" complained Jodie.

21–30. Answers will vary.

Test 9
1. It is my birthday tomorrow. (or exclamation mark)
2. Have you seen my hockey stick?
3. Your picture is amazing! (or full stop)
4. My friend Daniel is coming to play after school.
5. In March we are going to Paris on holiday.
6. How do you tie a bow?
7. That sandwich is enormous! (or full stop)
8. When Dad gets home we will all have dinner.
9. Is it getting dark yet?

10. Last Friday Megan had a fantastic party. (or exclamation mark)

11–20. Sentences will vary but should start with a capital letter and end with a full stop, question mark, or exclamation mark.

Test 10
1. flock of sheep
2. pack of cards
3. litter of puppies
4. bunch of flowers
5. pride of lions
6. swarm of flies
7. pod of whales
8. flights of stairs
9. herd of dairy cows
10. flock of seagulls
11. range   12. bunch
13. galaxy   14. army
15. gaggle   16. hive
17. pack   18. choir
19. team   20. fleet

21–30. Answers will vary but might include:
21. Mum bought a bunch of bananas from the greengrocer.
22. The class of students worked quietly.
23. A shoal of fish swam under the boat.
24. Beyond the meadow stood a forest of trees.
25. The special trailer contained a library of books.

26–30. Answers will vary but might include:
26. a hoof of horses
27. a heave of hippos
28. a trundle of tractors
29. a snout of pigs
30. a comfy of cushions

Test 11
1. bubble   2. hobble
3. riddle   4. muddle
5. litter   6. clatter
7. grinning   8. shudder
9. paddle   10. shutter
11. ripple   12. rabbit
13. hopping   14. letter
15. sudden   16. matter
17. wobble   18. dinner
19. cattle   20. winning
21. common   22. puddle
23. water   24. stubble
25. crater   26. table
27. nibble   28. adult
29. cutting   30. shuttle
31. kettle   32. rattle
33. apple   34. lorry
35. kitten   36. cherry
37. nappy   38. swimmer
39. cotton   40. mitten

Test 12

p									b
r			k						u
i		c							n
d	a	g	a	g	g	l	e	c
e	p	a					i	h
	f	l	o	c	k	t	
	l	a		h		t	
	e	x			e	e	
	e	y				r	
	t	s	w	a	r	m	d

Test 13
The hidden words are: nibble, sunny, topple, paddle, saddle, meddle, shatter, middle, gobble, tummy

Test 14
1. taller   2. smallest
3. shortest   4. loudest
5. faster   6. oldest
7. brighter   8. younger
9. greatest   10. colder
11. prettier   12. biggest
13. finer   14. bravest
15. silliest   16. fattest
17. safer   18. lovelier
19. spiciest   20. hotter
21. paler   22. palest
23. shinier   24. shiniest
25. fussier   26. fussiest
27. wider   28. widest
29. flatter   30. flattest
31. chillier   32. latest
33. fittest   34. earliest
35. naughtiest   36. cheekiest
37. dirtiest   38. angrier
39. noisiest   40. bigger

Test 15
1. thumb   2. knot
3. gnome   4. sign
5. rhyme   6. write
7. knee   8. calm
9. sword   10. chemist
11. would   12. stalk
13. when   14. scene
15. chalk   16. knock
17. wreck   18. gnaw
19. palm   20. numb
21. l   22. k
23. b   24. l
25. w   26. h
27. w   28. g
29. l   30. u
31. honest   32. lambs
33. should   34. why
35. half   36. knives
37. knight   38. talked
39. wrapped   40. wrong
41. yolk   42. ballet
43. catch   44. knows
45. doorknob   46. written
47. guaranteed   48. ghost
49. witch   50. white

Test 16
1. doesn't   2. shouldn't
3. won't   4. We'll
5. You'll   6. don't
7. she'll   8. I've
9. can't   10. would've
11. could not   12. I will/I shall
13. she is/she was   14. is not
15. were not   16. he will/he shall
17. it is   18. they have
19. we will/we shall   20. you will/you shall
21. would've   22. they'll
23. I'm   24. couldn't
25. won't   26. can't
27. you're   28. it'll
29. she'd   30. we're
31. wouldn't   32. I've
33. could've   34. it's
35. I'd   36. it'll
37. didn't   38. he's
39. aren't   40. isn't

Test 17
1. were   2. want
3. help   4. loses
5. goes   6. wait
7. love   8. wishes
9. send   10. am
11. goes   12. needs
13. enjoy/sister   14. plays/kittens
15. is/stars   16. picks
17. aren't   18. is
19. buy   20. talks
21. are   22. am
23. grows   24. is
25. is   26. is
27. is   28. are
29. lesson/start   30. say
31–40. Answers will vary.

Test 18
1. hairspray   2. doormat
3. postbox   4. goldfish
5. sunflower   6. moonlight
7. homework   8. kingfisher
9. eggshell   10. mankind
11. snow man   12. butter fly
13. rain bow   14. pea nut
15. suit case   16. news paper
17. straw berry   18. tooth paste
19. motor way   20. fire place
21. armchair   22. headache/stick
23. kneecap   24. necklace
25. football   26. handbag/ball/wash
27. fingernail   28. lipstick
29. hairbrush   30. mouthwash
31–40. Answers will vary.

Test 19
1. graceful   2. cheerful
3. bravely   4. kindly
5. colourful   6. quickly
7. hopeful   8. fortunately
9. completely   10. boastful
11. boldly   12. calmly
13. helpful   14. strangely
15. badly   16. boastful
17. brightly   18. careful

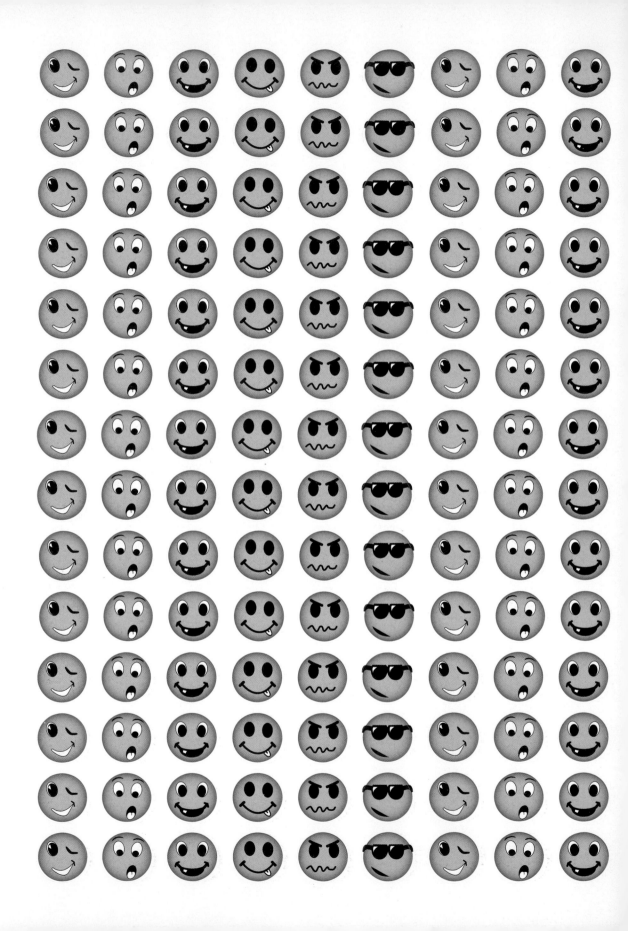

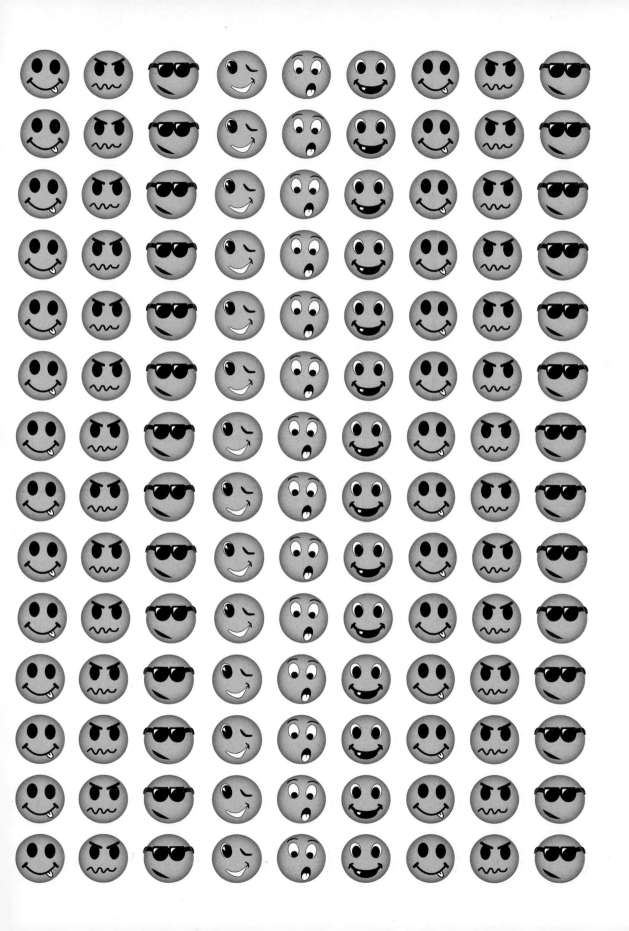

Column 1

19. clearly   20. friendly
21. beautiful   22. daintily
23. plentiful   24. prettily
25. dizzily   26. joyful
27. merrily   28. daily
29. playful   30. lazily
31. dangerously   32. clearly
33. spiteful   34. sadly
35. dreadful   36. carefully
37. gracefully   38. forgetful
39. peaceful   40. loudly

Test 20

1. bad   2. fast
3. soft   4. light
5. show   6. finish
7. quiet   8. awake
9. long   10. thick
11–30. Possible answers include:
11. new   12. lose
13. take   14. dry
15. out   16. light
17. empty   18. hot
19. weak   20. smooth
21. The little girl asked rudely for a cake.
22. We got to school so late that there was nobody in the playground.
23. Mum was surprised when she saw how untidy my bedroom was.
24. The television was off when we got home.
25. I did my homework carelessly.
26. Liam's football boots were clean.
27. Mohammed chose a dangerous place to cross the road.
28. Angie will not be able to go to the circus with us.
29. Mum asked me to close the windows.
30. The film was terrible.

Test 21

1. pink   2. funny
3. furious   4. naughty
5. huge   6. easy
7. little   8. white
9. beautiful   10. old
11–20. colours: green, turquoise, red
       size: massive, tiny, enormous
       moods: confused, excited, grateful, upset
21–30. Answers will vary but might include:
21. lazy   22. sharp
23. fierce   24. green
25. huge   26. dirty
27. old   28. exciting
29. delicious   30. delicate
31–40. Sentences will vary.

Test 22

Down:
1. sad   2. below
3. near   4. yes
5. low
Across:
6. down   7. lost
8. early   9. dry
10. sell

Column 2

Test 23

1–10. Award one mark for each of the features described.

Test 24

1–20. singular nouns: toy, horse, dress, garden, clock, rock, path, wish, jelly, rabbit
       plural nouns: trees, babies, bubbles, bushes, donkeys, boxes, eggs, matches, teeth, mice
21. bowls   22. watches
23. flowers   24. ladies
25. dishes   26. flashes
27. fairies   28. daisies
29. buses   30. classes
31. witches   32. homes
33. penguins   34. cities
35. walls   36. churches
37. armies   38. chairs
39. worries   40. crosses
41. blackberries   42. fields
43. bushes   44. berries
45. fingers   46. scratches
47. thorns   48. families
49. sandwiches   50. lunches

Test 25

1. The room was decorated with red, yellow and green balloons.
2. My favourite lessons at school are Games, Literacy and Art.
3. Tom, Jack and George are playing football.
4. We wrapped up warmly in hats, coats and scarves.
5. I packed pens, pencils and a ruler in my pencil case.
6. They went to the zoo, the circus and the beach over the summer.
7–8. There were cows, sheep, ponies and pigs at the farm.
9–10. Mum bought flour, eggs, sugar and butter to make the cake.
11. We put lemon, sugar and honey on our pancakes.
12. I go to Gym, Drama and Ballet after school.
13. My uncle has apple, pear and plum trees in his gardens.
14. Dad bought wallpaper, paint and brushes to decorate my bedroom.
15. Clover, daisies and buttercups grow in our lawn.
16. I have a dog, a cat and a rabbit.
17. Adam's favourite meal is fish fingers, chips and peas.
18. Mum added lettuce, tomato and cucumber to the salad.
19. The cake was covered in icing, candles and tiny pink flowers.
20. My notebook had red, blue and green stripes on the cover.
21–30. Sentences will vary.

Test 26

1–2. bat   3–4. match
5–6. bow   7–8. left
9–10. ring   11–12. bark
13–14. right   15–16. felt

Column 3

17–18. book   19–20. stamps
21–30. Answers will vary.

Test 27

1. The cat saw a mouse and ran after <u>it</u>.
2. The boys were tired when <u>they</u> got home.
3. Mr Brown read <u>us</u> a story in the afternoon.
4. Dad took Claire to gym club when <u>he</u> got home from work.
5. Tom looked for the shoes but could not find <u>them</u>.
6. Sita hid and Rachel hunted for <u>her</u>.
7. <u>We</u> watched a brilliant film last night.
8. The cat purred when Stella stroked <u>him</u>.
9. Mum sings when <u>she</u> is washing the dishes.
10. "Be careful when <u>you</u> cross the road," said Mrs Pearce.
11. she   12. me
13. he   14. us
15. it   16. I
17. they   18. you
19. We   20. him
21. he   22. they
23. we   24. us
25. her   26. him
27. them   28. it
29. she   30. they

Test 28

1. We were hot <u>because</u> the sun was shining.
2. Martin looked for the kitten <u>and</u> he found it under the table.
3. Chris loves ice-cream, <u>but</u> Dylan likes smoothies.
4. Mum thought the party finished too late; <u>however</u>, she said I could go.
5. <u>Although</u> he was tired, Tim wanted to play football.
6. The car broke down, <u>so</u> we had to catch the train.
7. Mrs Clarke was angry about the mess, <u>until</u> Paul explained it had been an accident.
8. Adele said she would be back early, <u>unless</u> the traffic was bad.
9. I watched TV <u>while</u> I ate my breakfast.
10. My baby sister giggles, <u>if</u> I tickle her.
11. before   12. so
13. since   14. or
15. but   16. and
17. because   18. unless
19. but   20. while
21–30. Answers will vary.

Test 29

1. first   2. last
3. then   4. afterwards
5. finally   6. later
7. now   8. next
9. eventually   10. earlier
11. during   12. while

13–20. A strange thing happened at breakfast. Dad lifted the cereal box, and all of the cornflakes poured out through a hole in the bottom of the box. <u>Next</u>, he went to make the toast and found that something had nibbled a tunnel right through the loaf. <u>After that</u>, Dad decided to have some crackers with cheese, instead. <u>When</u> he opened the fridge, though, he found that the cheese had been nibbled too!

<u>By then</u>, Mum had had an idea. She went into the lounge and looked at the cage where our hamster, Bertie, lives. The cage door was open. Bertie had escaped and was loose in our kitchen!

<u>After that</u>, we all began to look for Bertie. Dad looked behind the washing machine. <u>Then</u>, Mum looked carefully in the cupboards, <u>while</u> I searched under the table.

<u>At last</u> we found Bertie, curled up asleep in the sugar bowl!

21–30. Sentences will vary.

Test 30
1. Safiya skipped <u>happily</u> into school.
2. The dog stretched <u>lazily</u> in front of the fire.
3. Simon folded his clothes <u>neatly</u>.
4. Dean stomped <u>angrily</u> upstairs.
5. The cat leapt down <u>lightly</u> off the fence.
6. Sunlight shone <u>brightly</u> through the window.
7. Leona dances <u>beautifully</u>.
8. The children sat <u>quietly</u> while the teacher read the story.
9. The chick balanced <u>dangerously</u> on the edge of the nest.
10. Tommy <u>quickly</u> ran off to hide.

11–20. Answers will vary but might include:

11. Darren waved cheerfully at us.
12. We were totally confused by the homework.
13. Mum clapped proudly when I received the certificate.
14. Jake yawned sleepily.
15. The mouse crept silently past the sleeping cat.
16. Tim's coat got badly torn on the rusty nail.
17. The stars twinkled brightly in the night sky.
18. The twins clattered noisily through the front door.
19. Luke sat bravely while Mrs Smart bandaged his knee.
20. We waited patiently for the bus to arrive.
21. Malik
22. Sadie
23. Matthew
24. Mark
25. Sophie

26–30. Sentences will vary.

Circle a word in each sentence that should contain a silent letter. Write the word correctly at the end of the sentence.

31. The onest boy handed in the money he had found. _____

32. We fed the lams at the farm. _____

33. Dad shoud be back in time to see the show. _____

34. I wonder wy Mum is angry. _____

35. Chloe saved haf of her sweets for another day. _____

36. Stefan put the nives and forks on the table. _____

37. My favourite story is about a night on horseback. _____

38. The teacher taked about our school trip. _____

39. Katie rapped the present in colourful paper. _____

40. Lewis got three questions rong on his test. _____

41. The egg yok was bright yellow. _____

42. I love my balle class. _____

43. I hope I won't cach a cold before the party. _____

44. Sophie nows her times tables. _____

45. I turned the doornob but it was stuck. _____

46. Dan has ritten a letter to his friend in France. _____

47. The shop garanteed that the radio would work. _____

48. We told scary gost stories round the campfire. _____

49. I dressed as a wich for my part in the school play. _____

50. Sam has a wite rabbit as a pet. _____

/50

A contraction is when two words are joined together, with an apostrophe replacing the missing letters. Underline the contraction in each sentence.

1. Sonia doesn't like broccoli.

2. You shouldn't eat too many sweets.

3. Dad won't be home until after tea.

4. We'll see the film tomorrow morning.

5. You'll be cold if you do not wear a coat.

6. Make sure you don't forget your homework.

7. Mum says she'll play tennis later.

8. I've got a great new bike.

9. Mark can't play football because he has broken his leg.

10. I would've been on time but I missed the bus.

Write the words that have been joined in each contraction.

11. couldn't _____ _____

12. I'll _____ _____

13. she's _____ _____

14. isn't _____ _____

15. weren't _____ _____

16. he'll _____ _____

17. it's _____ _____

18. they've _____ _____

19. we'll _____ _____

20. you'll _____ _____

Tick the correct contracted form for these words.

21. would have   ☐ would've   ☐ wouldv'e

22. they will   ☐ they'll   ☐ they'l

23. I am   ☐ I'me   ☐ I'm

24. could not   ☐ couldnt'   ☐ couldn't

25. will not   ☐ willn't   ☐ won't

26. cannot   ☐ can't   ☐ cann't

27. you are   ☐ you're   ☐ your'e

28. it will   ☐ itl'l   ☐ it'll

29. she would   ☐ she'ld   ☐ she'd

30. we are   ☐ we're   ☐ wer're

Write the correct contracted forms for these pairs of words.

31. would not   _____

32. I have   _____

33. could have   _____

34. it is   _____

35. I would   _____

36. it will   _____

37. did not   _____

38. he is   _____

39. are not   _____

40. is not   _____

/40

Making sense

Circle the correct verb from the brackets to complete each sentence.

1. We [was were] late for school because the car broke down.

2. I [want wants] to be a fireman when I grow up.

3. My cousins [helps help] me with my homework.

4. My brother [loses lose] his things all the time.

5. My sister [goes go] to a different school now.

6. I overslept so my friends had to [waits wait] for me.

7. The boys in my class [love loves] playing football.

8. Although my sister is tall, she [wish wishes] she was even taller.

9. We always [sends send] a Christmas card to my auntie.

10. I [am is are] seven years old.

Underline the mistake in each sentence.

11. My parents goes to parents' evening tonight.

12. I needs a new pair of shoes.

13. My sister enjoy singing in the school choir.

14. The kittens plays with the ball of wool.

15. The stars is shining brightly tonight.

16. We picks our favourite pizza from the menu.

17. It aren't polite to stare at people.

18. I is afraid of the dark.

19. Tara buy sweets on the way home from school.

20. Our teacher is angry if we talks in class.

21. My dad are great at playing football.

22. A new family am moving in next door.

23. When I grows up, I want to be a nurse.

24. The children is all excited about the party.

25. Eloise and Charlotte is my best friends.

26. The boys will be in trouble if they is late for school again.

27. These questions is very difficult.

28. I are learning to play the drums.

29. The swimming lesson start at half past four.

30. Mr Briggs say we have worked very hard.

Write a sentence including each phrase.

31. I am _____

32. she is _____

33. we eat _____

34. he eats _____

35. it goes _____

36. they go _____

37. you walk _____

38. she walks _____

39. I love _____

40. he loves _____

/40

Compound words

Complete the word sums to make compound words.

1. hair + spray = _____
2. door + mat = _____
3. post + box = _____
4. gold + fish = _____
5. sun + flower = _____
6. moon + light = _____
7. home + work = _____
8. king + fisher = _____
9. egg + shell = _____
10. man + kind = _____

Write the two words which make up each of these compound words.

11. snowman _____ _____

12. butterfly _____ _____

13. rainbow _____ _____

14. peanut _____ _____

15. suitcase _____ _____

16. newspaper _____ _____

17. strawberry _____ _____

18. toothpaste _____ _____

19. motorway _____ _____

20. fireplace _____ _____

Compound words

Add a word from the box to each of these body parts to make a compound word.

nail	ache	wash	lace
bag	ball	brush	
chair		cap	stick

21. arm _____

22. head _____

23. knee _____

24. neck _____

25. foot _____

26. hand _____

27. finger _____

28. lip _____

29. hair _____

30. mouth _____

Add a word to each of these words to make a new compound word.

31. school _____

32. book _____

33. fire _____

34. tea _____

35. bed _____

36. key _____

37. sea _____

38. clock _____

39. black _____

40. work _____

/40

Suffixes *ful* and *ly*

A suffix is a group of letters that can be added to the end of some words to change their meanings. Underline the suffix in each word.

1. graceful

2. cheerful

3. bravely

4. kindly

5. colourful

6. quickly

7. hopeful

8. fortunately

9. completely

10. boastful

Tick the correct suffix for each word.

11. bold   ☐ boldful   ☐ boldly

12. calm   ☐ calmly   ☐ calmful

13. help   ☐ helpful   ☐ helply

14. strange   ☐ strangeful   ☐ strangely

15. bad   ☐ badful   ☐ badly

16. boast   ☐ boastful   ☐ boastly

17. bright   ☐ brightly   ☐ brightful

18. care   ☐ careful   ☐ carely

19. clear   ☐ clearly   ☐ clearful

20. friend   ☐ friendful   ☐ friendly

Try these trickier word sums. Remember to think carefully about whether to change the spelling of the completed word.

21. beauty + ful = _____

22. dainty + ly = _____

23. plenty + ful = _____

24. pretty + ly = _____

25. dizzy + ly = _____

26. joy + ful = _____

27. merry + ly = _____

28. day + ly = _____

29. play + ful = _____

30. lazy + ly = _____

Underline a word in each sentence that ends with the suffix **ful** or **ly**.

31. The boy was dangerously close to the kerb.

32. Alice was clearly very excited about her party.

33. The spiteful girl pinched her little sister.

34. Sadly, Matthew was ill so he missed the school trip.

35. Mrs Pearce has a dreadful cold today.

36. Tristan coloured the picture carefully.

37. The ballet dancers leapt gracefully across the stage.

38. Samuel is so forgetful that he left his homework on the bus!

39. The forest glade was calm and peaceful.

40. The balloon burst loudly.

/40

Opposites

Draw lines to match the words with their opposites.

1.	good	soft
2.	slow	thick
3.	hard	finish
4.	dark	awake
5.	hide	bad
6.	start	light
7.	loud	long
8.	asleep	fast
9.	short	quiet
10.	thin	show

Write an opposite for each word.

11. old _____

12. win _____

13. give _____

14. wet _____

15. in _____

16. heavy _____

17. full _____

18. cold _____

19. strong _____

20. rough _____

Write each sentence again, replacing the bold words with their opposites to change the meaning of the sentence.

21. The little girl asked **politely** for a cake.

_____

22. We got to school so **early** that there was nobody in the playground.

_____

23. Mum was surprised when she saw how **tidy** my bedroom was.

_____

24. The television was **on** when we got home.

_____

25. I did my homework **carefully**.

_____

26. Liam's football boots were **dirty**.

_____

27. Mohammed chose a **safe** place to cross the road.

_____

28. Angie **will** be able to go to the circus with us.

_____

29. Mum asked me to **open** the windows.

_____

30. The film was **brilliant**.

_____

/30

Adjectives

Adjectives are words that describe nouns. Underline the adjective in each sentence.

1. Maddie chose pink wallpaper for her bedroom.

2. We saw a funny film at the cinema.

3. Mr Smith was furious with the boys.

4. The naughty puppy chewed the slipper.

5. Jack chose a huge piece of cake.

6. The maths homework was easy.

7. A little girl played on the swings.

8. Annie keeps white mice as pets.

9. The singer wore a beautiful dress.

10. The old car broke down on the motorway.

Sort the adjectives below into the groups on the chart.

| 11. green | 12. massive | 13. turquoise | 14. confused | 15. excited |
| 16. tiny | 17. red | 18. enormous | 19. grateful | 20. upset |

colour	size	moods

Add a suitable adjective to complete each sentence.

21. The _____ boy had not done his homework.

22. The broken plate had _____ edges.

23. My favourite book is about a _____ dragon.

24. Danny ate a crunchy _____ apple.

25. The fireworks made a _____ banging noise.

26. Amy's football boots were _____ after the match.

27. The _____ bike was rusty and scratched.

28. Susie's party is going to be _____.

29. Mum's pizzas are _____.

30. _____ snowflakes drifted gently to the ground.

Write your own sentences using these adjectives.

31. purple

_____

32. pretty

_____

33. furry

_____

34. spooky

_____

35. gentle

_____

36. silly

_____

37. dangerous

_____

38. untidy

_____

39. exhausted

_____

40. rare

_____

/40

Fun with opposites

Find the opposite of each clue word and write it in the crossword grid.

Down:

1. happy
2. above
3. far
4. no
5. high

Across:

6. up
7. found
8. late
9. wet
10. buy

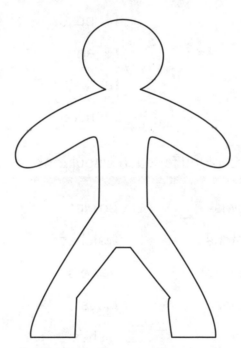

Adjective fun

Use these adjectival phrases to help you design and colour a funny clown. Use the outline below to help you.

1. enormous shoes
2. bright yellow hair
3. colourful coat
4. purple spotty bow-tie
5. funny make-up
6. shiny red nose
7. stripy trousers
8. scruffy hat
9. pretty flower on the hat
10. huge orange gloves

/10

Plurals

Singular means one of something. Plural means more than one.
Underline the singular nouns and circle the plurals.

1. toy
2. horse
3. trees
4. dress
5. garden
6. babies
7. bubbles
8. clock
9. bushes
10. donkeys
11. rock
12. path
13. wish
14. boxes
15. jelly
16. eggs
17. matches
18. teeth
19. rabbit
20. mice

Tick the correctly spelled plural for each singular noun.

21. bowl   ☐ bowls   ☐ bowles

22. watch   ☐ watchs   ☐ watches

23. flower   ☐ floweres   ☐ flowers

24. lady   ☐ ladies   ☐ ladys

25. dish   ☐ dishs   ☐ dishes

26. flash   ☐ flashes   ☐ flashs

27. fairy   ☐ fairies   ☐ fairys

28. daisy   ☐ daisyes   ☐ daisies

29. bus   ☐ buses   ☐ buss

30. class   ☐ classs   ☐ classes

Write the plurals for these words.

31. witch _____

32. home _____

33. penguin _____

34. city _____

35. wall _____

36. church _____

37. army _____

38. chair _____

39. worry _____

40. cross _____

Find ten incorrectly spelled plurals in this piece of text, then write the correct spellings below.

Every autumn I would go and pick blackberrys with my friend Kate. We walked across the fieldes to find the best bushs and picked as many berryes as we could. Our fingeres would be covered in purple stains and scratchs from the thornes. Then we would take the fruit home to our familys.

Mum used to make blackberry jam to put in the sandwichs we had in our packed lunchs at school.

41. _____   42. _____

43. _____   44. _____

45. _____   46. _____

47. _____   48. _____

49. _____   50. _____

/50

We can use commas to separate the things in a list.
Add commas to these sentences.

1. The room was decorated with red yellow and green balloons.

2. My favourite lessons at school are Games Literacy and Art.

3. Tom Jack and George are playing football.

4. We wrapped up warmly in hats coats and scarves.

5. I packed pens pencils and a ruler in my pencil case.

6. They went to the zoo the circus and the beach over the summer.

7–8. There were cows sheep ponies and pigs at the farm.

9–10. Mum bought flour eggs sugar and butter to make the cake.

Underline the comma mistake in each sentence,
then add the comma in the correct place.

11. We put lemon sugar, and honey on our pancakes.

12. I go to, Gym Drama and Ballet after school.

13. My uncle has apple pear and plum, trees in his gardens.

14. Dad, bought wallpaper paint and brushes to decorate my bedroom.

15. Clover daisies, and buttercups grow in our lawn.

16. I have a dog a cat and a, rabbit.

17. Adam's favourite meal is fish, fingers chips and peas.

18. Mum added lettuce tomato and cucumber to, the salad.

19. The cake was covered, in icing candles and tiny pink flowers.

20. My notebook had red blue and green stripes on, the cover.

Write a sentence including these things, in a list.

21. apples pears bananas

_____

22. football cricket rugby

_____

23. rabbits foxes badgers

_____

24. sandwiches cakes crisps

_____

25. buses trains motorbikes

_____

26. red white blue

_____

27. knives forks spoons

_____

28. Tuesday Wednesday Thursday

_____

29. books magazines newspapers

_____

30. Katie Amy Eve

_____

/30

Homonyms are words that look and sound the same but mean something different. Underline the homonym that appears in each pair of sentences.

1–2. A bat flew in front of the moon.

Chris forgot his cricket bat.

3–4. Dad used a match to light the candle.

Our school team won the football match.

5–6. The archer had a bow and arrow.

I can tie my shoelaces in a bow.

7–8. There are no apples left in the fruit bowl.

My brother writes with his left hand.

9–10. The diamond ring sparkled in the moonlight.

Dad waited for the phone to ring.

11–12. We did tree bark rubbings at school today.

The postman made our dogs bark.

13–14. Sophia got all of her spellings right.

You must turn right at the traffic lights.

15–16. I made a purse out of red felt.

Scott felt better when he woke up.

17–18. Ella chose a new reading book.

Mum phoned the cinema to book the tickets.

19–20. Sudip bought some stamps at the post office.

My baby sister stamps her foot when she is angry.

Write your own sentences using these homonyms.
They have been put in phrases to help you.

21. cross the road

_____

22. the teacher was cross

_____

23. blue hair band

_____

24. school brass band

_____

25. came back

_____

26. sore back

_____

27. block the sink

_____

28. building block

_____

29. light as a feather

_____

30. electric light

_____

/30

Pronouns are words you can use instead of nouns.
They are words like **he**, **she**, **they** or **it**.
Underline the pronoun in each sentence.

1. The cat saw a mouse and ran after it.

2. The boys were tired when they got home.

3. Mr Brown read us a story in the afternoon.

4. Dad took Claire to gym club when he got home from work.

5. Tom looked for the shoes but could not find them.

6. Sita hid and Rachel hunted for her.

7. We watched a brilliant film last night.

8. The cat purred when Stella stroked him.

9. Mum sings when she is washing the dishes.

10. "Be careful when you cross the road," said Mrs Pearce.

Circle the correct pronoun from the brackets to complete each sentence.

11. Katie was amazed when [she he] opened the present.

12. Grandma bought [we me] a fishing rod for my birthday.

13. Adam hurt his knee when [he they] fell over.

14. When my cousins came over, Mum made [they us] a cake.

15. Marcus mended the car when [she it] broke down.

16. "[I She] don't like cabbage!" complained Ahmed.

17. The children tidied the classroom before [us they] went home.

18. Eating fruit and vegetables is very good for [you he].

19. [I We] were late for school because of the traffic.

20. Mark is ill so the class made [him it] a card.

Write these sentences again, replacing the bold words with a suitable pronoun.

21. Max was hungry so **Max** made a sandwich.

_____

22. Before Mum and Dad went out, **Mum and Dad** kissed me goodnight.

_____

23. My brother and I are going to the cinema if **my brother and I** have finished our homework.

_____

24. Sanjiv and I rang Mum when the show finished and she picked **Sanjiv and I** up.

_____

25. When Jenny's tea was ready, Dad called **Jenny** in from the garden.

_____

26. Jonathan went up in assembly and the teacher gave **Jonathan** a certificate.

_____

27. The dog saw the ducks and ran after **the ducks**.

_____

28. I dropped the cup and **the cup** broke.

_____

29. After **Lucy** missed the bus, Lucy had to walk home.

_____

30. When **the twins** have their next birthday, the twins will be ten years old.

_____

/30

Conjunctions

Conjunctions like **and**, **but** or **because** join parts of a sentence together. Circle the conjunction in each sentence.

1. We were hot because the sun was shining.

2. Martin looked for the kitten and he found it under the table.

3. Chris loves ice-cream, but Dylan likes smoothies.

4. Mum thought the party finished too late; however, she said I could go.

5. Although he was tired, Tim wanted to play football.

6. The car broke down, so we had to catch the train.

7. Mrs Clarke was angry about the mess, until Paul explained it had been an accident.

8. Adele said she would be back early, unless the traffic was bad.

9. I watched TV while I ate my breakfast.

10. My baby sister giggles, if I tickle her.

Choose a suitable conjunction from the box to complete each sentence.

but	so	because	or
but	before	and	
unless	since	while	

11. Luckily, we got home _____ it began to rain.

12. Ali waters the plant, _____ it will grow.

13. David has been reading a book _____ he got home from school.

14. I can save my pocket money, _____ I can spend it on a magazine.

15. The cake looked delicious _____ it tasted awful!

16. Dad took us to a theme park _____ we went on a roller coaster.

17. I love gymnastics _____ it is fun.

18. _____ I find my trainers, I will have to miss the football match.

19. The coat was lovely, _____ it was too small.

20. We watched carefully, _____ Mr Reed showed us how to make cookies.

> Think of interesting ways to complete these sentences.

21. It was my birthday, so _____.

22. Andrew was excited because _____.

23. My brother wanted to buy some sweets, but _____.

24. I entered the competition and _____.

25. Unless it stops raining, _____.

26. I would love a pet cat or _____.

27. _____ while we waited for the bus.

28. _____ before he went to work.

29. Although she worked hard, _____.

30. _____ until Dad came home from work.

/30

Find and copy 12 words in the box that could be used to show when something happened.

first	last	black	small
tired	then	afterwards	
afraid	backwards	finally	funny
later	different	next	
eventually	fallen	earlier	lost
now	calm	during	
hurry	wish	while	

1. _____

2. _____

3. _____

4. _____

5. _____

6. _____

7. _____

8. _____

9. _____

10. _____

11. _____

12. _____

> Underline eight time words and phrases in this story.

13–20.

A strange thing happened at breakfast. Dad lifted the cereal box, and all of the cornflakes poured out through a hole in the bottom of the box. Next, he went to make the toast and found that something had nibbled a tunnel right through the loaf. After that, Dad decided to have some crackers with cheese, instead. When he opened the fridge, though, he found that the cheese had been nibbled too!

By then, Mum had had an idea. She went into the lounge and looked at the cage where our hamster, Bertie, lives. The cage door was open. Bertie had escaped and was loose in our kitchen!

After that, we all began to look for Bertie. Dad looked behind the washing machine. Then, Mum looked carefully in the cupboards, while I searched under the table.

At last we found Bertie, curled up asleep in the sugar bowl!

> Write your own sentences using these time words.

21. after _____

22. then _____

23. eventually _____

24. soon _____

25. during _____

26. when _____

27. finally _____

28. while _____

29. in the end _____

30. first _____

/30

Adverbs help us to describe the way things happen, by adding meaning to verbs. Underline the adverb in each sentence.

1. Safiya skipped happily into school.

2. The dog stretched lazily in front of the fire.

3. Simon folded his clothes neatly.

4. Dean stomped angrily upstairs.

5. The cat leapt down lightly off the fence.

6. Sunlight shone brightly through the window.

7. Leona dances beautifully.

8. The children sat quietly while the teacher read the story.

9. The chick balanced dangerously on the edge of the nest.

10. Tommy quickly ran off to hide.

Add an adverb to complete each sentence.

11. Darren waved _____ at us.

12. We were _____ confused by the homework.

13. Mum clapped _____ when I received the certificate.

14. Jake yawned _____.

15. The mouse crept _____ past the sleeping cat.

16. Tim's coat got _____ torn on the rusty nail.

17. The stars twinkled _____ in the night sky.

18. The twins clattered _____ through the front door.

19. Luke sat _____ while Mrs Smart bandaged his knee.

20. We waited _____ for the bus to arrive.

Use the adverbs to help you circle the answer to each question.

21. Patrick ran slowly. Malik ran quickly.

Who won the race?   Patrick   Malik

22. Nicole chewed the cake thoughtfully. Sadie chewed frantically.

Who finished their cake first?   Sadie   Nicole

23. Fiona read quietly. Matthew read loudly.

Who made the most noise?   Matthew   Fiona

24. Mark worked carefully. Mandy worked carelessly.

Who did the best work?   Mark   Mandy

25. Larissa arranged her things tidily. Sophie arranged hers chaotically.

Who could not find her pencil case? Larissa   Sophie

Write your own sentences using these adverbs.

26. sadly _____

27. rudely _____

28. safely _____

29. kindly _____

30. nervously _____

/30

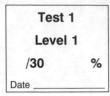

Test 1 Level 1 /30 % Date ___	Test 2 Level 2 /30 % Date ___	Test 3 Level 2 /30 % Date ___	Test 4 Level 2 /40 % Date ___	Test 5 Level 3 /40 % Date ___

Test 1

Level 1

/30   %

Date _____

Test 2

Level 2

/30   %

Date _____

Test 3

Level 2

/30   %

Date _____

Test 4

Level 2

/40   %

Date _____

Test 5

Level 3

/40   %

Date _____

Test 6

Level 3

/40   %

Date _____

Test 7

Level 3

/30   %

Date _____

Test 8

Level 3

/30   %

Date _____

Test 9

Level 2

/20   %

Date _____

Test 10

Level 3

/30   %

Date _____

Test 11

Level 2

/40   %

Date _____

Test 12

Did you find all of the words? Colour this red if it took you less than 10 minutes, colour it blue if it took longer.

Date _____

Test 13

Did you find all of the words? Colour this red if it took you less than 10 minutes, colour it blue if it took longer.

Date _____

Test 14

Level 3

/40   %

Date _____

Test 15

Level 3

/50   %

Date _____

Test 16

Level 3

/40   %

Date _____

Test 17

Level 3

/40   %

Date _____

Test 18

Level 2

/40   %

Date _____

Test 19

Level 3

/40   %

Date _____

Test 20

Level 2

/30   %

Date _____

Test 21

Level 2

/40   %

Date _____

Test 22

If you got all of the clues in less than 10 minutes, colour this red. Colour it blue if it took longer.

Date _____

Test 23

Did you dress the clown? Colour this red if it took you less than 10 minutes, colour it blue if it took longer.

Date _____

Test 24

Level 2

/50   %

Date _____

Test 25

Level 2

/30   %

Date _____

Test 26

Level 2

/30   %

Date _____

Test 27

Level 2

/30   %

Date _____

Test 28

Level 3

/30   %

Date _____

Test 29

Level 3

/30   %

Date _____

Test 30

Level 3

/30   %

Date _____

Colour each box in the correct colour to show how many questions you got right.

0%–20% = yellow, 21%–50% = green, 51%–70% = blue, 71%–100% = red

This will help you to monitor your progress.